Echoes of Faith Plus

Companion Booklet

Catholic Morality

Module Consultant
Richard Reichert, MA

Theological Consultant
Richard C. Sparks, CSP, PhD

Echoes of Faith Plus Program Directors

Edmund F. Gordon, MA
National Conference for Catechetical Leadership

Jo Rotunno, MA
RCL Benziger

Educational Consultant
Judith Deckers, MEd

Contributors

Marie Egan, IHM, STD
Donna Toliver Grimes, MA
Bill Huebsch, MA
Rev. Frank McNulty, STD
Most Rev. Sylvester Ryan, MA

**A Project of the
National Conference for Catechetical Leadership
Produced by RCL Benziger**

Special Thanks

We wish to extend special thanks to Rev. John West, STD, who was instrumental in the development of the original Catholic Morality module. We would also like to thank the following individuals whose interviews appear on the DVD for this module.

Rev. Bryan Massingale, STD

William Mattison, PhD

Nihil Obstat
Rev. Msgr. Robert Coerver
Censor Librorum

Imprimatur
† Most Reverend Kevin J. Farrell, DD, Bishop of Dallas

December 4, 2007

The Nihil Obstat and Imprimatur are official declarations that the material reviewed is free of doctrinal or moral error. No implication is contained therein that those granting the Nihil Obstat and Imprimatur agree with the contents, opinions, or statements expressed.

Send all inquiries to:
RCL Benziger
200 East Bethany Drive
Allen, TX 75002-3804

Toll Free   877-275-4725
Fax   800-688-8356

Visit us at   www.RCLBenziger.com
              www.EchoesofFaith.com
              www.FaithFirst.com
              www.WholeCommunityCatechesis.com

Printed in the United States of America

20587   0-7829-1153-6

1 2 3 4 5 6 7 8 9 10
07 08 09 10 11 12 13

ACKNOWLEDGMENTS

Excerpts from English translation of the *Catechism of the Catholic Church* for the United States of America Copyright © 1994, United States Catholic Conference, Inc.—Libreria Editrice Vaticana. English translation of the: *Catechism of the Catholic Church Modifications from the Editio Typica* Copyright © 1997, United States Catholic Conference, Inc.—Libreria Editrice Vaticana. Used with permission.

Scripture quotations from *New Revised Standard Version Bible: Catholic Edition,* copyright 1989, 1993 Division of Christian Education of the National Council of the Churches of Christ in the United States of America. Used by permission. All rights reserved.

Excerpts from *General Directory for Catechesis*, copyright © 1997, United States Conference of Catholic Bishops—Libreria Editrice Vaticana. All rights reserved. No part of this work may be reproduced or transmitted in any form without the permission in writing from the copyright holder.

Excerpts from *National Directory for Catechesis*, copyright © 2005, United States Conference of Catholic Bishops, Washington, DC. Used with permission. All rights reserved. No part of this work may be reproduced or transmitted in any form without the permission in writing from the copyright holder.

Contents

Welcome to *Echoes of Faith Plus!*

The *General Directory for Catechesis (GDC)* tells us, "The Lord Jesus invites men and women, in a special way, to follow him, teacher and formator of disciples. This personal call of Jesus Christ and its relationship to him are the true moving forces of catechetical activity" (*GDC* 231). This call needs a response from you in order to flourish. As you begin your ministry as a catechist, you will need to deepen your knowledge of the faith and of the Gospel. You will need to develop techniques and skills for presenting the faith and adapting it to your group of adults, children, or youth. Catechesis is always about communicating the faith!

Echoes of Faith Plus has been developed by the National Conference for Catechetical Leadership (NCCL) to provide you with the basic tools to begin your ministry as a catechist. It is being used in more than one hundred dioceses in the United States and Canada and has proven to be an effective process to set you on the way to have a wonderful experience as a catechist.

We have designed this program for use in varied settings. If you are working alone on a module, it is important that you link up with someone, e.g., your local DRE, catechist trainer, or parish priest. Since catechesis always involves communication, it is important that you have someone with whom to discuss your new learning, to ask questions, and to try out new ideas!

Catechesis is an activity of the whole Church. As a catechist you join a worldwide network of catechists who support each other in prayer. The Church is depending on you to bring "tidings of great joy" to the classrooms, religious education centers, homes, and wherever catechesis takes place.

May the Holy Spirit guide you, energize you, and sustain you!

Lee Nagel
NCCL Executive Director

Edmund F. Gordon
NCCL Project Director

A Project of the National Conference for Catechetical Leadership Produced by RCL Benziger

How to Use
Echoes of Faith Plus

Echoes of Faith Plus is a basic-level, video-assisted resource for the formation, training, and enrichment of catechists in parish and Catholic school settings. *Echoes* was sponsored and developed by the National Conference for Catechetical Leadership (NCCL) and produced by RCL Benziger.

The *Echoes* project is divided into three series of modules. Each series relates to one of the three aspects of catechist formation explained in the *General Directory for Catechesis*—being, knowing, and *savoir-faire.* (See *GDC* 238.)

The Catechist: (being)	Three modules on the vocation and roles of the catechist, plus first steps for getting started in the ministry
Methodology: (savoir-faire)	Four modules for different grade levels of children and youth. One module for facilitators of adult faith formation. One overview module on human and faith development
Theology: (knowing)	Four modules treating the four pillars of the *Catechism of the Catholic Church,* plus a fifth module introducing Sacred Scripture. (Note: These modules can also be used for general adult faith formation.)

The main components of each module are:

- **A DVD.** The DVD is comprised of a four–segment video process related to the module content plus two related expert interviews.
- **A Companion Booklet.** The booklet anchors the *Echoes* process. Each booklet begins with an article for spiritual formation and a prayer. The booklet then provides a four–segment process of reflection, discussion, faith sharing, and prayer as the participant moves back and forth between the DVD and print material. Each segment includes a follow-up enrichment article. The back of the booklet offers related articles and resources. These resources and two bonus interviews on the DVD could provide material for additional sessions.
- **A CD-ROM.** The CD-ROM features compressed files that offer a way to review the basic video content of the four segments on a computer. However, it does not include the interviews found on the DVD. The CD-ROM is included at no charge with each companion booklet.

The length of time required to complete each module varies with the length of the DVD and how it is used. This module should take approximately four hours to process. The key to success with *Echoes of Faith Plus* is your willingness to engage in the complete process. Ideally, your reflection process will take place in a group setting that models the kind of Christian community you wish to establish in your own catechesis. If you must process the module alone, share your insights later in a group setting or with a friend in ministry.

Catechists do not merely instruct their students about Christ; they lead them to him.

National Directory for Catechesis (NDC) 55E

Visit http://www. EchoesofFaith.com for additional resources to enrich your catechetical ministry.

Catholic Morality: *A Way of Living*

by Reverend Louis J. Cameli, STD

In one way or another, we are all teachers of morality. If you are a catechist or parent, you have a special role to play. In so many decisive ways, you shape the conscience of those entrusted to you. Of course, there are many factors in the moral formation of children—some positive and some not so helpful. In this mix, catechists and parents have a privileged role and a real possibility of shaping moral sensibilities that will lead to good choices and conformity with God's will for us.

Our own sense of the moral life will inevitably permeate our teaching and our example. So, it is critical that we be in touch with a genuine sense of Catholic morality for ourselves. That will be the source for our teaching and formational work with others.

In our culture, the popular conception of morality is that of a restrictive set of rules that forbids certain behaviors. In this framework, morality is an imposition, something we would rather not have to deal with but are forced to face. There are many in the family of faith who have this sense of morality and moral life—extrinsic rules, imposed, and grudgingly accepted. An authentic sense of the moral life is exactly the opposite.

St. Paul proposes such an authentic sense in his letter to the Colossians. In so many ways, these words of Paul capture his foundational understanding of Christian morality.

> *So, if you have been raised with Christ, seek the things that are above . . . Put to death, therefore, whatever in you is earthly: fornication, impurity, passion, evil desire, and greed (which is idolatry) . . . As God's chosen one, holy and beloved, clothe yourselves with compassion, kindness, humility, meekness, and patience . . . And whatever you do, in word or deed, do everything in the name of the Lord Jesus, giving thanks to God the Father through him.* (Colossians 3:1, 5, 12, 17)

Morality is, first of all, a way of deciding and acting. It is a way of living. In Paul's perspective, Christians find their way of living by looking at

> *The moral life means letting faith suffuse everything, every dimension, every action.*

their identity in Christ. Precisely because they are "raised with Christ" and have become one with him, Christians will necessarily decide and live in a certain way. Far from being a set of extrinsic or imposed rules, morality flows from the deepest source of our identity as new creatures in Jesus Christ. If we really know who we are, we will know the kind of life to which we are called. It will be a natural and logical consequence of our identity in Christ. And it has no room for whatever is incompatible with that identity, for example, impurity, greed, anger, or idolatry.

Furthermore, morality is not reserved for a sector of life, a particular piece of living. Paul clearly says ". . . whatever you do, in word or deed, do everything in the name of the Lord Jesus" (Colossians 3:17). In other words, the moral life means letting faith suffuse everything, every dimension, every action. We are no longer in the realm of rules for this or that. We have a vision that directs the whole of our lives.

Certainly, some of the particulars of Catholic morality need to be studied and properly assimilated. First, however, we must come to terms with the deepest foundation for that morality. It is who we are in Jesus Christ—an identity that summons us to live in a transformed way.

For Reflection

- Who helped you the most to come to your understanding of what it means to live a moral life?
- What Scripture passages help to remind you of your identity and responsibilities as a follower of Christ?

Louis J. Cameli is a priest of the Archdiocese of Chicago and pastor of Divine Savior Parish in Norridge, Illinois. He completed his theological studies at the Gregorian University in Rome and obtained a doctorate in theology with a specialization in spirituality. He is the former director of ongoing formation of priests in the Archdiocese of Chicago and director of the Cardinal Stritch Retreat House, Mundelein, Illinois. In February, 2002, he received the Pope John XXIII Award from the National Organization for the Continuing Education of Roman Catholic Clergy (NOCERCC) for his contributions to the continuing education and ongoing formation of priests. He has authored numerous books on spirituality and also served as a writer and theological consultant for RCL Benziger's *Faith First* and *Faith First Legacy Edition* K-8 curriculum.

Faithful to the Light

Lord Jesus,

*You **light the way** for us*

in our journey through life.

As your followers, clothe us

*in a garment woven with **compassion** for others;*

*with **kindness** toward those who may only know your love through us;*

*with **humility,** so we will remember that we are only reflections of you,*

the one, true, Son of God.

*Clothe us with **gentleness,** that we may never do harm to another;*

*with **patience,** that we may take the time to listen and to forgive.*

*Let us **shed your light** wherever we go,*

*as we try to **give witness** to you and*

***bring God's reign** into our world.*

We ask for all these gifts

in your holy name.

Amen.

Overview: Catholic Morality Module

The third pillar, or section, of the *Catechism of the Catholic Church*, "Life in Christ," addresses the topic of morality. Morality deals with how we are to live as Christians. We seek this understanding in and through Jesus, who describes himself as "the way, and the truth, and the life" (John 14:6). The goal of this module is to explore the foundations of Catholic morality and the practice of the moral life.

As you explore the content of this module, you will engage in a process of faith reflection using three components: a DVD, this companion booklet, and a CD-ROM. See page 5 for an explanation of how these components complement one another. You began the process on pages 6 and 7 with a reflection on Jesus, our model in living a moral life. On page 11 you will describe some of your present understandings of morality.

Each of the four segments in this module is divided into two parts. Here is an overview of the topics that each segment of the booklet and DVD will explore:

1. **Foundations of the Moral Life**
   Part 1: What Is Morality?
   Part 2: What Is Virtue?
2. **Objective and Subjective Morality**
   Part 1: What Is Objective Morality?
   Part 2: What Is Subjective Morality?
3. **The Morality of Human Actions**
   Part 1: What Makes an Action Moral?
   Part 2: What Is Sin?
4. **Conscience and God's Law**
   Part 1: What Is Conscience?
   Part 2: Why Are There Commandments?

You will find a six-page booklet process for each segment to help you reflect on the DVD content and apply what you have learned. Here is the structure you will find:

1. **Introduction:** The goal and objectives for each session, plus an opening reflection question
2. **Looking Ahead—Presentation:** A video overview for each part and space for writing
3. **Looking Back—Reflection:** Three reflection questions for each of the two parts
4. **Looking Beyond—Application:** An opportunity to integrate Catholic teaching with daily life

This module is only a brief introduction to the vast tradition of Catholic morality. As you continue to read, study, reflect, and attend classes and workshops, you will grow in knowledge and insight. Try to participate in the learning process of this module in a group setting. If circumstances require that you work independently, find at least one other person with whom you can share your reflections.

Morality — How we stand before God and before one another"

Father Richard Sparks, a Paulist priest, divides his time between giving ethics workshops, serving as an ethical consultant to various hospitals, and ministering as associate pastor. Father Sparks has a Ph.D. in Christian Ethics from the Catholic University of America in Washington, D.C. He is the author of two books and numerous articles.

Before You Begin

As you begin your study of the foundations of Catholic morality, take a few moments to describe your present understanding of the meaning of this term. Place words on the lines that come to mind as you consider this term, add as many lines as you wish. Share your responses with your group.

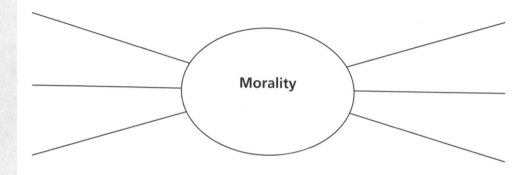

**For to me,
living is
Christ . . .**

Philippians 1:21

Foundations of the Moral Life

Morality is the task of distinguishing between good and evil and applying these distinctions to human behavior. The two underlying moral principles of our Judaeo-Christian tradition are the dignity of each human person as a child of God, and the vocation of God's children to live in friendship with God and one another. The good is whatever supports human dignity and fosters our relationship with God and the community. Evil is whatever weakens or destroys them. The study of morality is to help us live our vocation as disciples of Jesus in the midst of daily life. In this module you will also explore the nature of virtues—those habits or qualities of our character that enable us to live a moral life. We acquire virtues both as a grace from God and as a result of conscientious daily choice. Through the virtues we try to develop a lifestyle of selfless love by following the example of Jesus.

> There are two ways, one of life, the other of death; but between the two there is a great difference.
> *Didache 1,1*

Goal

To acquire a deeper understanding of the meaning and foundations of Christian morality and the virtues

Learning Objectives

- To describe a Christian under-standing of morality

- To explain the two basic principles of Christian morality: human dignity and community

- To explain the meaning of virtues and their value in living a moral life

Exercise

Take a few moments to reflect on the following question. Then discuss it with another person or with your group.

Describe a person you know who lives the values of Jesus. What moral qualities does that person have?

Looking Ahead

Part 1: What Is Morality?

Part 1 of this segment explores the general question, "What is morality?" Below you will find an outline of the principal content of the DVD that accompanies Part 1 of this segment. You may wish to refer to this outline as you watch the DVD. Below the outline, there is space for you to jot down questions that occur to you during and after the viewing.

Video Outline

- Short on-the-street interviews with a number of individuals who explain their understanding of morality
- Interviews with experts who describe the relationship between the moral principles of human dignity and community
- An introduction to two couples whose stories will be explored during the module

Comments and Questions

Use the space below to list questions, feelings, or ideas that occur to you as you view the video.

> **The dignity of the human person is rooted in his creation in the image and likeness of God; it is fulfilled in his vocation to divine beatitude.**
>
> **Catechism of the Catholic Church (CCC) 1700**

Watch Segment 1, Part 1 of the DVD or CD-ROM now.

Looking Back

Part 1: What Is Morality?

Reflect silently on one or more of the questions below and then jot down your response(s). Then share your thoughts with another person or with a group.

1. Reflect on the statements of the three moral theologians on the video about the meaning of morality. Then summarize in your own words the Church's understanding of Christian morality.

2. Recall the two principles of human dignity and community described by Father Sparks in the video. Describe a time when your appreciation of one of these principles assisted you in making a moral decision.

3. Jesus is the model for the moral life. Name three values you have learned from the message of Jesus that have helped you to live as a moral person.

Remember . . .

Morality is life in Christ.

•

Morality consists of values, choices, and actions.

•

Human dignity and community are the bases of morality.

•

The Trinity offers us a model of community.

Looking Ahead

Part 2: What Is Virtue?

Part 2 of segment 1 explores the question, "What is virtue?" Below you will find an outline of the principal content of the DVD that accompanies this part. You may wish to refer to this outline as you watch the DVD. Below the outline, there is space for you to jot down questions that occur to you during and after the viewing.

Video Outline

- Definitions of virtue by experts in moral theology
- An explanation of the cardinal virtues
- The example of a young married couple who face a moral crisis and the way in which their decision-making process incorporates the four cardinal virtues

Comments and Questions

Use the space below to list questions, feelings, or ideas that occur to you as you view the video.

> **Conscience is man's most secret sanctuary. There he is alone with God whose voice echoes in his depths.**
> *Gaudium et spes 16*

> **Watch Segment 1, Part 2 of the DVD or CD-ROM now.**

Looking Back

Part 2: What Is Virtue?

Reflect silently on one or more of the questions below and then jot down your response(s). Then share your thoughts with another person or with a group.

1. The video identifies and describes the cardinal virtues. Describe the ways you practice them. When has the practice of one of the cardinal virtues helped you to make a moral decision?

2. Reflecting on the McNaughtons' story in the video, explain how they lived their faith in making their moral decision.

3. Recall the definition of beatitude or happiness given in the video, then write or draw your understanding of true happiness.

   Happiness is . . .

Looking Beyond

Virtues are not our own until they become habits we live by. The exercise below will help you to practice living the values of Jesus.

LIVING IN CHRIST

The video describes the cardinal virtues as hinge virtues in living a Christian life. Choose one of these situations below and describe how the practice of one of the cardinal virtues has or could assist you in resolving an issue in your own life related to this situation.

Racial or ethnic prejudice

Excessive materialism

Overemphasis on competition

FOR CATECHISTS AND PARENTS

Encourage children to choose a virtue to practice each week and to jot down their successes in living up to its demands.

What Did I Learn?

In this space summarize the most important insights you gained in this segment.

What Will I Change?

In this space write one thing you will do differently as a catechist because of what you learned in this segment.

Catholic Morality

by Most Reverend Sylvester Ryan

Simply expressed, Catholic morality is following the teachings and example of Jesus Christ. Jesus revealed to us God's unconditional love, a love so strong that even sin cannot deter or diminish it. God's love, revealed in Christ and through the Holy Spirit, invites all people to respond in faith, hope, and love.

God's love always respects human freedom. The Catholic moral life is the unfolding story of the human response or refusal of this invitation. What, then, does the moral life look like? What is its shape or character?

Character speaks of the kinds of persons we are, or are meant to be. Jesus spoke of character in his Sermon on the Mount by emphasizing what kinds of persons will enter the kingdom of God. (Matthew 5:1–12)

The constant conviction of our Catholic moral and spiritual tradition has been that as human persons are transformed by the grace of redemption they can achieve a virtuous life, or moral character, which in turn can lead to God. A virtue, as described in the *Catechism of the Catholic Church*, "is an habitual and firm disposition to do the good." (*CCC* 1803) The goal of Catholic moral life, then, is to become a virtuous person—to develop the inclination and the skills to strive for what is *right* and *good*.

To pursue and choose the good in concrete actions requires the development of a mature conscience. Conscience speaks in the inmost soul of an obligation to do only what is right and good. But conscience does not reveal the specifics of right and wrong. All virtuous people look for assistance and enlightenment in order to make correct ethical judgments. They must do so prayerfully, seeking guidance in the teachings of Jesus Christ and the Church's magisterium, and conferring where needed with pastors, scholars, and theologians.

Catholics recognize that certain actions are objectively right or wrong. The teachings of Jesus, the Ten Commandments, and the magisterium of the Church present us with enduring objective truths. Yet moral choices take place within the realities of sin and human frailty, personal growth, and cultural differences. These

Bishop Sylvester D. Ryan is the retired bishop of Monterey. A priest of the archdiocese of Los Angeles, he has served as president and rector of St. John's Seminary College in Camarillo and pastor of Our Lady of Lourdes Parish in Sunland-Tujunga.

Bishop Ryan has served as Episcopal Liaison for the National Conference for Catechetical Leadership and chairman of the National Conference of Catholic Bishops' Ad Hoc Committee on Stewardship. Bishop Ryan is a former president of the California Bishops' Conference.

elements may lead to mistaken notions of what is right and good. Sincere moral effort, however, always unfolds within the deeper reality of the mercy and healing of Christ's grace, especially available in the sacraments of Reconciliation and Eucharist.

Conscience speaks in the inmost soul of an obligation to do only what is right and good.

In addition, our modern world presents us with new and complex moral issues. These require study and reflection by the Church, and consultation with the community and experts in the human sciences. Complex situations demand rigorous application of sound moral principles.

The community of faith is critical to the development of a Catholic morality. Jesus was not only concerned about individual conversion, but also about a people called to live in a covenant relationship with God. Saint Paul, for example, frequently addressed himself to the moral or immoral behavior of individuals in terms of how this behavior built up or tore down the Christian community. (1 Corinthians 5)

Catholics, then, must recognize the effect of their actions on how the church community fulfills its role as a sign and a sacrament of the redeeming Christ in the world. We are all challenged by our baptism, not only to choose the good ourselves, but to assist others to choose "speaking the truth with love." (Ephesians 4:15)

● ● ● *For Reflection* ● ● ●

- How has the community of faith assisted you in the development of your moral life?

- When has it been the hardest to "speak the truth with love," both to yourself and to others?

2

Objective and Subjective Morality

In our highly individualistic society, many see morality mainly as a matter of personal choice. However, morality is based on certain unchanging objective truths that can be arrived at through reason. To ignore this objective aspect would be to plunge humanity into relativism and confusion. We have access to this objective truth through reason, the wisdom of our leaders, and the collective wisdom of the ages. For us Catholics this collective wisdom includes the teaching of the Church. The availability of objective moral truth does not free us, however, from the personal responsibility to apply these truths to the concrete circumstances of our lives. This application introduces a subjective element to our moral choices.

Goal

To explore the relationship between objective moral norms and the subjective elements involved in moral decision making

Learning Objectives

- To define objective morality and subjective morality

- To identify the sources for arriving at objective moral truth and to appreciate the Church's unique role in this process

- To apply objective moral truths to a concrete subjective situation

Exercise

Take a few moments to reflect on the following. Then discuss your response with another person or with your group.

Name some moral truths you have been able to discover simply by the use of your reason.

Prayer

God of infinite wisdom, you sent us your Spirit to guide us in making good choices each day. Help us listen to your voice whispering within us so that all the choices we make will conform us more completely to your holy will. We ask this in Jesus' name. Amen.

Looking Ahead

Part 1: What Is Objective Morality?

Part 1 of this segment explores the nature of objective morality. Below you will find an outline of the principal content of the DVD that accompanies Part 1 of this segment. You may wish to refer to this outline as you watch the DVD. Below the outline, there is space for you to jot down questions that occur to you during and after the viewing.

Video Outline

- Individuals describing their understanding of actions that are always wrong
- Theological experts describing the role of reason in determining the difference between good and evil
- A layman describing his efforts to live a moral life
- Experts describing the sources for arriving at objective moral truth

Comments and Questions

Use the space below to list questions, feelings, or ideas that occur to you as you view the video.

The natural law is nothing other than the light of understanding placed in us by God; through it we know what we must do and what we must avoid.

St. Thomas Aquinas
Collationes in decem praeceptis I

Watch Segment 2, Part 1 of the DVD or CD-ROM now.

Looking Back

Part 1: What Is Objective Morality?

Reflect silently on one or more of the questions below and then jot down your response(s). Then share your thoughts with another person or with a group.

1. Ron Jackson describes how he and his wife drew up a moral code that expressed the values that their family tries to live by. In the space below, describe the moral values that are held most sacred within your family.

   Our Family's Values

2. Recall a movie or television show you have seen in the past month. What objective moral truth(s) were affirmed or challenged by this media? In what ways?

3. Jesus told us that "[A]nd you will know the truth, and the truth will make you free" (John 8:32). How does knowing an objective moral truth free you rather than impede you when you make a personal choice?

Remember . . .

There is objective truth and goodness.

•

Natural law indicates the basic moral sense that allows us to see the good.

•

The Magisterium is the teaching authority of the Pope and bishops of the Church.

Looking Ahead

Part 2: What Is Subjective Morality?

Part 2 of segment 2 explores the nature of subjective morality. Below you will find an outline of the principal content of the DVD that accompanies this part. You may wish to refer to this outline as you watch the DVD. Below the outline, there is space for you to jot down questions that occur to you during and after the viewing.

Video Outline

- A group of teenagers discussing their views on moral issues
- Experts describing the objective and subjective dimensions to morality
- A description of the role of personal responsibility in arriving at correct moral decisions

Comments and Questions

Use the space below to list questions, feelings, or ideas that occur to you as you view the video.

SOURCES OF OBJECTIVE MORALITY

- **Sacred Scripture**

- **The lives of the saints**

- **The lives of contemporary witnesses**

- **Human reason**

- **Catholic teaching**

Watch Segment 2, Part 2 of the DVD or CD-ROM now.

Looking Back

Part 2: What Is Subjective Morality?

Reflect silently on one or more of the questions below and then jot down your response(s). Then share your thoughts with another person or with a group.

1. Father Sparks speaks of the need to love the person even as we may challenge some of his or her actions. Give some examples in our contemporary culture where this understanding could improve the quality of dialogue among persons or groups.

2. The students in the video describe a school environment in which their peers seem to place little value on objective moral rules. What example can you offer them through which you came to understand the value of an objective code of conduct?

3. In light of the ideas expressed in the video, respond to the following statement: "The Church has no right telling me what to do in my private life."

Remember . . .

Objective morality deals with the moral rightness or wrongness of an act.

•

Subjective morality deals with the sincerity of a person's moral decision.

•

A subjective moral decision may be sincere yet morally incorrect.

•

Capacity for right judgment determines one's level of moral responsibility.

•

God continues to love us despite our wrong choices.

Looking Beyond

In the video you learned that objective moral norms remain unchanging, even though subjective circumstances might affect a person's culpability. The exercise below will help you to analyze a moral choice from this standpoint.

LIVING IN CHRIST

Consider one of the following situations. Name an objective moral truth that could apply to it. Then list some subjective factors which might influence the person's culpability. Discuss your response with another person or group.

1. A parent writes a book report for a child who has not finished reading the book on time.

2. A politician running for office fails to reveal an embarrassing incident from his past to his constituents.

Objective Moral Value	Subjective Factors

What Did I Learn?

In this space summarize the most important insights you gained in this segment.

What Will I Change?

In this space write one thing you will do differently as a catechist because of what you learned in this segment.

  (P)

FOR CATECHISTS AND PARENTS

With children, especially younger ones, focus on teaching the objective moral norms rather than exploring possible reasons for not following them.

Objective and Subjective Morality: A Key Moral Distinction

by Richard C. Sparks, C.S.P.

Every time I hear someone say, "Just follow your conscience," I cringe a little. It's just not that simple! Yes, we are obliged to follow what we personally believe to be the right course of action. Yes, ultimately we must weigh all our moral options and then make a decision "in good conscience." However, being sincere or meaning well is not the total measure of whether we've made an objectively right decision. And that distinction between subjective sincerity and objective rightness or wrongness is central in our Catholic Christian moral tradition.

In the ethnic Catholic ethos of our parents' and grandparents' generations much moral energy was focused on actions, particularly immoral or sinful actions. It seemed as if morality was somewhat outside of us, a list of do's and don'ts decreed by God, the government, our parents, or some other authority. If you broke the laws or rules you were considered wrong and deserving of punishment, with little wiggle room for exceptions, situational excuses, or good intentions.

In recent decades the pendulum in our society seems to have swung almost to the opposite extreme. Nowadays, if we say that someone did something wrong, many people respond by suggesting that we're "old-fashioned," "out of it," or are being "too judgmental." Their presumption seems to be that if a person acts sincerely and means well, that somehow their action is thereby blameless or even praiseworthy.

Not necessarily so! What about a happy, organized-crime assassin, a contented rapist, or a smiling child abuser? Just because they "feel good," or freely opt to do a given deed, does not automatically mean that they've thought things through wisely or have formed their conscience rightly.

There are all sorts of subjective factors which may color one's culpability (praise or blame). For example, due to mental illness or temporary insanity,

Father Richard Sparks, a Paulist priest, divides his time between giving ethics workshops, serving as an ethical consultant to various hospitals, and ministering as associate pastor.

Father Sparks has a PhD in Christian Ethics from the Catholic University of America in Washington, DC. He is the author of two books and numerous articles.

some people may choose to do horribly destructive actions to themselves or to others. While we seek professional help for them, we do not say that their choices (e.g., to kill or to rape) are good, objectively right ones. Subjectively, they may not be fully to blame for actions that we consider objectively wrong.

> *Teach what is objectively good with clarity and conviction, but tread gently in assigning subjective credit or blame.*

So too, even those with full mental competency still may be missing some of the facts or ethical insight necessary to make sound moral judgments. While ignorance lessens the level of personal responsibility, it does not thereby make their actions or choices right or good. In addition to ignorance, there may also be questions of long-standing family or cultural biases that impact to varying degrees one's praise- or blame-worthiness. Still, being blinded by one's past does not completely excuse nor alter the general or objective judgment about certain actions being morally right or wrong.

In a classroom or educational setting, we ought to teach what is objectively good and right with clarity and conviction, while at the same time treading gently and pastorally in assigning credit or blame to a given person. Like Moses standing humbly before God on Mt. Sinai, we too should remove our sandals and enter gently whenever we deal with anyone's interior state of soul. In the realm of moral decision-making and conscience formation we are standing on holy ground.

● ● ● **For Reflection** ● ● ●

What steps can we take that will help our moral choices to be both objectively right and subjectively sincere?

3

The Morality of Human Actions

Human actions are a combination of action, intention and circumstances. A critical task of conscience in evaluating an action is to evaluate the circumstances surrounding it. While circumstances cannot alter the objective nature of an act, they can significantly alter the subjective moral culpability of the individual who carries it out. Sin occurs when we freely make choices we know to be morally wrong. Some sins are always seriously sinful by their very nature. Others may be less offensive in themselves, but are actions that, if repeated over time, could become habitual and lead to more serious sin. Sinful choices always disrupt our relationship with God to some degree.

Goal

To establish criteria for determining the morality or immorality of a human action

Learning Objectives

- To explain how object, intention and circumstance affect the quality of a moral action

- To describe the role that the common good plays in the morality of human actions

- To define the nature of sin and describe the criteria for determining the seriousness of sin

Exercise

Take a few moments to reflect on the following. Then discuss it with another person or with your group.

In what way could circumstances play a role in determining the morality of an action?

Prayer

Loving God, you have shown us the path to life through your Son, Jesus Christ. As we make the daily choices of our lives, help us to be intentional about our actions and to try always to choose the good. We ask for the guidance of the Holy Spirit so that all our actions will be a reflection of your love for us. Amen.

Looking Ahead

Part 1: What Makes an Action Moral?

The first part of this segment explores the nature of objective morality. Below you will find an outline of the principal content of the DVD for this part. You may wish to refer to this outline as you watch the DVD. Below the outline, there is space for you to jot down questions that occur to you during and after the viewing.

Video Outline

- A businessman discusses the ethical issues that arise in his daily decision-making.
- A theologian describes the triple-font theory that describes the three criteria (action, intention, and circumstance) for moral decisions.
- A description by a theologian of false criteria that some people use to guide their moral lives.
- A theologian describes the important sources to turn to in making moral decisions.

Comments and Questions

Use the space below to list questions, feelings, or ideas that occur to you as you view the video.

> **The morality of human acts depends on: the object chosen; the end in view or the intention; the circumstances of the action.**
> *CCC 1750*

> **Watch Segment 3, Part 1 of the DVD or CD-ROM now.**

Looking Back

Part 1: What Makes an Action Moral?

Reflect silently on one or more of the questions below and then jot down your response(s). Then share your thoughts with another person or with a group.

1. A woman decides to go into a convenience store and steal a carton of milk. What combination of object, intention, and circumstances might affect her moral culpability?

2. Recall the Gospel account of Peter's betrayal of Jesus (Luke 22:54–62). Describe the intention and circumstances of Peter's action.

3. Fr. Massingale points out in the video that every action has a social dimension. Consider each of the following situations. Describe what implications each might have for the common good.

Situation	Implication for the Common Good
A woman shares gossip she has heard about another person	
A man decides to understate his income on his tax return	
A parent criticizes a child in front of others	

Remember . . .

Circumstances may change the moral rightness of an act.

•

Circumstances affect a person's responsibility.

•

Christians have a social responsibility.

•

Perfect freedom is directed toward goodness.

Looking Ahead

Part 2: What Is Sin?

The second part of this segment explores the nature of sin. Below you will find an outline of the principal content of the DVD that accompanies this part. You may wish to refer to this outline as you watch the DVD. Below the outline, there is space for you to jot down questions that occur to you during and after the viewing.

> Sin is an offense against reason, truth, and right conscience; it is failure in genuine love of God and neighbor . . .
>
> **CCC 1849**

Video Outline

- A husband and wife describe decisions that had serious consequences for their marriage.
- A group of individuals describe their understanding of sin.
- Theologians discuss the following topics:
    - —the consequences of sin
    - —the distinction between mortal and venial sin
    - —the criteria for serious sin

Comments and Questions

Use the space below to list questions, feelings, or ideas that occur to you as you view the video.

> **Watch Segment 3, Part 2 of the DVD or CD-ROM now.**

Looking Back

Part 2: What Is Sin?

Reflect silently on one or more of the questions below and then jot down your response(s). Then share your thoughts with another person or with a group.

1. Why are venial sins a cause for concern in an individual's moral life?

2. Recall the story of Bob and Alicia Waning. What qualities allowed them to break the patterns of behavior which might have led to the permanent ending of their marriage?

3. Consider each of the following three hobbies. What set of circumstances might cause each of these actions to become an occasion of sin for the person who enjoys them?

   - Cooking

   - Playing on a softball team

   - Hiking

Remember . . .

Sin is a negative moral action contrary to God's law.

•

Sin involves the breaking of a relationship with God, people, or oneself.

•

Certain moral actions are always wrong.

•

Venial sins are lesser offenses which can lead to more serious sin.

Looking Beyond

In this segment you learned more about the nature of sin and criteria for judging the morality of human actions. The exercise below will help you practice living the values of Jesus in daily life.

LIVING OUR FAITH

The examination of conscience is a traditional means by which Christians evaluate their actions daily, particularly in preparation for the Sacrament of Reconciliation. List three important questions you might ask yourself to help you evaluate the progress of your moral life.

> It is important for every person to be sufficiently present to himself in order to hear and follow the voice of his conscience.
> **CCC 1779**

Many young children have not experienced serious sin. Use concrete imagery to help them understand what it means to rupture their relationship with God or another person.

What Did I Learn?

In this space summarize the most important insights you gained in this segment.

What Will I Change?

In this space write one thing you will do differently as a catechist because of what you learned in this segment.

32

Catholic Morality

Grace and Justification

by Bill Huebsch

Grace is first and foremost a gift from God. It is a gift unearned, and in a sense, undeserved. It is the gift of the Holy Spirit—and it is this Spirit that justifies and sanctifies us. In the end, all grace leads us to conversion. It leads us to turn from sin and embrace God's constant offer of divine love.

When Saint Paul speaks of our justification (Romans 3:21–26) he refers to this right standing before God which was effected for us by the death and resurrection of Jesus. Another good word for this is holiness. This holiness is the immediate outcome of grace, when we accept it and follow where it leads us. We also call this sanctification.

We don't make ourselves holy. God makes us holy. We are, in a sense, adopted by God. We are not justified or made holy by any initiative on our part. God is the one to whom we owe everything. The fact that God has freely chosen to touch our lives with God's power, in other words, to offer us grace, is pure generosity and love. Even our ability to respond comes from God's initiative. God, in other words, both offers us love and makes it possible for us to respond. God is all in all for us.

As Christians, we experience God's active pursuit of us through the life and death of Jesus, the most excellent work of God's plan for our salvation. Through Christ, God has communicated and revealed to us how deeply God desires us to be with him, and for us to live in the same love shared by the Trinity.

Sanctifying grace is the habitual inclination on our part to seek God. Everyone is given this grace. God never leaves us and the sign of God's ever-present offer of love is the Church. We can always come back. We can always come home to the Church. We can always be reconciled because the offer of God's love is never withdrawn from any human being.

Actual grace, on the other hand, results from God's interventions in our lives through the sacraments, Sacred Scripture, and other means, including the love of those around us. Such actual graces may occur in our lives

Bill Huebsch is a theologian, lecturer, and author whose home is in Pine City, Minnesota. His academic background includes a Bachelor of Arts degree from the University of North Dakota and a Master of Arts degree from the Catholic Theological Union of Chicago, where he focused on the history of reform in the Church. Bill worked in pastoral ministry for over ten years and has worked for four religion publishers, most recently as President of Twenty-third Publications in New London, CT. Among his most recent publications are *Growing Faith,* an adult formation program, *Into the Fields,* a catechist formation program, and *Dreams and Visions: Pastoral Planning for Adult Faith Formation,* all from Twenty-third Publications.

JUSTIFICATION IN CHRIST

- **is conferred through Baptism.**

- **sanctifies and renews us.**

- **allows the acceptance of God's love.**

- **pours faith, hope, and love into our hearts.**

- **makes possible the coopera-tion between God's grace and our human freedom.**

Based on CCC 1987–1995

when we are first called and beginning our journey toward holiness, or they may occur along the road as we are ever more deeply immersed into the Christian life.

In any case, God calls us to make a free response. There is within us an inborn longing for God, a yearning for truth. But we are created in God's own image and, therefore, we have the freedom to enter into

There is within us an inborn longing for God, a yearning for truth.

communion with God or not. And when, prompted by the grace of the Holy Spirit, we do enter into God's life, we find there our own most authentic lives. Whatever virtue we have acquired through education or formation is purified and elevated by this grace. With God's continuing assistance, character is forged and, despite the wound of sin, we truly become the children of God.

For Reflection

Your good actions are a free response to the saving love of God that you have already been given. What difference does this make to you in the way you view your moral life?

Conscience and God's Law

Conscience involves both a capacity for making moral judgments and the process of arriving at such judgments. Although everyone without serious mental defect has the innate capacity to form moral judgments, this capacity develops as we mature. We must ultimately follow our conscience, but we must always seek to inform our conscience. The Ten Commandments, viewed from the standpoint of reason alone, offer us timeless and universal moral principles necessary for living together in keeping with our dignity as children of God. When viewed with the eyes of faith they describe what might be considered a moral minimum, the starting point for moral growth. All that they contain can be reduced to Jesus' two great commandments of love of God and love of neighbor. Rather than restrictions on our freedom, they guide us to use our freedom properly in ways that will result in true happiness.

Goal

To appreciate the role of conscience in moral decision-making and to acknowledge the importance of informing it

Learning Objectives

- To describe the nature of conscience

- To explain the process of informing one's conscience

- To relate the Ten Commandments and Jesus' Law of Love and to understand more fully their relationship to the Christian life

Exercise

Take a few moments to reflect on the following question. Then discuss it with another person or with your group.

What is your conscience? What role do the Ten Commandments play in helping you to follow your conscience?

Prayer

Dear God, you have placed your Law within us to guide us as we try to do your will. Help us to judge always according to this standard of goodness that you have placed within us so that we may act always with justice, compassion, and love. We ask this in the name of your Son, who shows us the path to eternal life with you. Amen.

Looking Ahead

Part 1: What Is Conscience?

The first part of this segment explores the nature of conscience. Below you will find an outline of the principal content of the DVD for this part. You may wish to refer to the video outline as you watch the DVD. Below the outline, there is space for you to jot down questions that occur to you during and after the viewing.

Video Outline

- A group of individuals describe what morality means to them.
- Theologians describe the innate sense of right and wrong that is our conscience.
- A married couple describe a critical bioethical choice they face with their child.
- Theologians describe the importance of informing one's conscience and ways of doing so.
- A theologian describes the inner peace that can come from making a carefully considered moral decision.

Comments and Questions

Use the space below to list questions, feelings, or ideas that occur to you as you view the video.

SOURCES FOR INFORMING CONSCIENCE

- **Scripture**
- **Church Teaching**
- **Insights of theologians and the believing community**
- **Prayer to the Holy Spirit**

Watch Segment 4, Part 1 of the DVD or CD-ROM now.

Catholic Morality

Looking Back

Part 1: What Is Conscience?

Reflect silently on one or more of the questions below and then jot down your response(s). Then share your thoughts with another person or with a group.

1. Complete the following three statements in your own words.

   Conscience is . . .

   Informing one's conscience means . . .

   I feel at peace when I . . .

2. The McNaughton's story describes a family struggling with a complex moral issue. Describe the process they followed in coming to their decision and eventually experiencing a sense of inner peace.

3. What sources have you turned to when you made a serious moral decision? How did each assist you in making your decision?

Source	Influence on My Decision

Remember . . .

Conscience is our innate sense of right and wrong.

•

Conscience needs to be informed by the truth.

•

We have a moral obligation to inform and follow our consciences.

Looking Ahead

Part 2: Why Are There Commandments?

The second part of this segment treats the Ten Commandments as a basis for the moral life. Below you will find an outline of the principal content of the DVD that accompanies this part. You may wish to refer to this outline as you watch the DVD. Below the outline, there is space for you to jot down questions that occur to you during and after the viewing.

Video Outline

- Individuals describe their understanding of the meaning of the Commandments.
- Two theologians define the Commandments and describe the two divisions within them: love of God and love of neighbor.
- The Commandments are described as minimal standards of conduct for every person who seeks to live a moral life.
- Theologians describe how the moral life flows from our beliefs, our participation in the sacraments, and our prayer.

Comments and Questions

Use the space below to list questions, feelings, or ideas that occur to you as you view the video.

> **The Commandments take on their full meaning within the covenant.**
> *CCC 2061*

Watch Segment 4, Part 2 of the DVD or CD-ROM now.

Catholic Morality

Looking Back

Part 2: Why Are There Commandments?

Reflect silently on one or more of the questions below and then jot down your response(s). Then share your thoughts with another person or with a group.

1. Dr. Egan tells us in the video that Jesus' Law of Love is a maximalist ethic which invites us to challenge our present behaviors. Choose one of the Ten Commandments. List some of the positive ways a Christian can keep it in ways that are beyond the letter of the law.

Commandment	Response

2. Practically speaking, what does it mean on a daily basis to love God with your whole heart, soul and mind?

3. Imagine that all the nations of the world agreed to adjust the laws to reflect the values expressed in the Ten Commandments. List five changes that would occur.

Looking Beyond

In this segment you learned that the Ten Commandments provide a standard for moral living that all are called to follow. The following exercise will help you see how following the Ten Commandments leads to a way of life that touches every aspect of Christian living.

LIVING OUR FAITH

Imagine that you are asked at an ecumenical gathering to explain the following statement to the group: Our Catholic moral life is the way that we express all that we believe, celebrate, and pray. How would you respond?

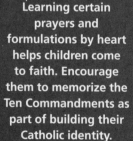
What Did I Learn?

In this space summarize the most important insights you gained in this segment.

What Will I Change?

In this space write one thing you will do differently as a catechist because of what you learned in this segment.

Praying the News

Place sections of daily newspapers or news magazines on a table, and invite each participant to choose one and read silently from it. Invite participants to gather around a prayer center, holding the news in their hands as they pray the following.

Leader: Creator God, the news we read each day fills us with both joy and sorrow, as we reflect on the ways your love is accepted or refused by your people. We place before you now all the stories that we have reflected upon, for even reports of sadness or refusal to love can be transformed by your grace.

Leader: Let us reflect.
A reading from the Gospel of Matthew
(Matthew 25:31–40)

Leader: Let us pray for victims.
(Pause for spontaneous prayers.)

Leader: Let us reflect.
A reading from the Gospel of Matthew
(Matthew 5:1–11)

Leader: Let us pray for persecutors and oppressors, and for all who are the instruments of violence and injustice.
(Pause for spontaneous prayers.)

Leader: Let us reflect.
A reading from the Gospel of Luke
(Luke 6:27–31)

Leader: Let us pray for the grace not to judge those who appear not to do your will.
(Pause for spontaneous prayers.)

Leader: Let us pray together the prayer that Jesus gave us, that God's love will continue to transform our world, and that we may be God's instruments until the day when the reign of God is fulfilled.

All: Our Father . . .

Conscience and God's Law

The Role of the Commandments in Our Moral Life

by Richard Reichert

Richard Reichert is retired as a consultant for youth and adult catechesis in the diocese of Green Bay, Wisconsin, a position he held for twenty-five years. He has written numerous monographs and articles on catechesis and has written several catechetical textbook series. Mr. Reichert has served as a member of the board of directors for the National Conference for Catechetical Leadership. He holds master's degrees from the University of Notre Dame, Indiana and from Loyola University of Chicago.

In our Catholic tradition the Ten Commandments have always been considered humanity's foundational moral principles. The *Catechism of the Catholic Church* tells us that these principles are accessible to reason. (CCC, 2071) As such they represent the essential moral requirements of the natural law upon which all human society rests, regardless of its religious beliefs. They outline our basic moral responsibilities toward our Creator, toward one another, and toward all creation.

Though accessible to reason, the Commandments are also an integral part of God's revelation. When viewed through the eyes of faith they assume even greater significance as guides to moral behavior. This significance is best understood within the context of the covenant in which the Commandments were first revealed by God.

In ancient times a covenant was a solemn pact freely entered into by two parties in which each agreed to assume certain responsibilities. The two parties might or might not be equals. In either case, the critical feature was that both parties entered into the covenant freely. The covenant also contained agreed-upon sanctions (punishments, curses, forfeitures) if one of the parties broke the agreement.

It is against this background of ancient covenants that we can best understand the covenant entered into by God and the Hebrew people at Mount Sinai. God, having freed the Hebrew people from their slavery in Egypt, claims them as God's own people and promises to continue to protect and guide them forever. For their part the Hebrew people promise to keep the Commandments God presents to them through Moses.

Several points deserve mention here. First, God takes the initiative in seeking out, rescuing, and entering into a covenant with the Hebrews. Second, the Hebrews remain free to reject the covenant God offers them.

Third, the Commandments are not treated as impersonal or abstract moral principles, but as interpersonal responsibilities God and the Hebrews mutually assume in an I-thou relationship. "I will be your God and you shall be my people" (Jeremiah 7:23).

What are the implication of these observations? When the Commandments are viewed in faith as part of a covenant between God and ourselves, the motivation for observing them becomes one of maintaining our personal relationship, our friendship with God. Love rather than fear urges us to live up to our responsibilities as God's friends and chosen people.

Jesus viewed the Commandments that way. His own moral teaching was clearly rooted in this tradition of the Hebrew covenant. But Jesus goes on to reveal in word and action the full implications of God's covenant or commitment to humanity and what our own response should be. He shows that we need to go beyond the letter to the spirit behind the law. His Sermon on the Mount is a summary of this expanded understanding of what our covenant of friendship with God involves.

The Commandments represent the essential moral requirements of the natural law upon which all human society rests.

So, the moral teaching of the gospel does not replace the Commandments. Rather it represents the flowering or fullness of the foundational moral principles which they contain.

For Reflection

How has your understanding of the nature of God's covenant been expanded by this article?

Moral Decision Making

by Reverend Frank McNulty

Reverend Frank J. McNulty is a noted preacher, teacher, and author. He attended Immaculate Conception Seminary in Darlington, New Jersey, and earned an S.T.L. (licentiate in sacred theology degree) and an S.T.D. (doctorate in sacred theology degree).

Sometimes we can gain moral insight from a television program. Recently I watched a program in which a pastor is consulted in the Sacrament of Reconciliation by a young woman who finds herself pregnant and considering an abortion. The priest tells her to "follow your conscience," and little more. Later, she consults another priest who explains the Church's position on abortion, but offers no further advice.

Both priests' approaches are extreme. The first might be called "interiorizing." The latter could be called "exteriorizing." The first priest threw the ball completely into the young woman's court; the second priest carried the ball for her. One priest forgot that her complete value system had a role to play; the other forgot that an essential part of that value system is a freedom of conscience. But what does that freedom entail?

The *Catechism of the Catholic Church* tells us that "Conscience is a judgment of reason whereby the human person recognizes the moral quality of a concrete act." (CCC, 1778) It can be something like a Geiger counter making appropriate noises when you approach a sinful choice. But if you only interiorize and make an isolated decision, you may ignore history, the gospel, or the Church. You may ignore the rights of others.

The opposite extreme has its own set of dangers. You might ignore your conscience and turn the choice over solely to someone else—a confessor, a pastor, a theologian, or a church teaching. However, we must not evade our personal responsibility by leaving it entirely to others to make our moral judgments.

The determination of what is right and what is wrong is accomplished by a person, and there is much more to a person than intellect or this particular moment of existence. We all see life through our own filters. These filters come from our emotions, attitudes, prejudices, and personal histories. They come from our environment, culture, families, and peer groups. To simply listen to our interior Geiger counter would be so simple. To simply do what someone else tells us to do might be equally simple. But neither would represent a sufficiently conscientious decision.

What is the middle path? The Church teaches us that we must always obey the "certain judgment" of our conscience. (CCC, 1790) Yet we have an obligation to see that we have informed our conscience to the best of our ability and to follow our best judgment. We must thoughtfully ponder the relevant circumstances and all the values involved. Yet we will need outside help in complicated situations. Prayer will be an essential help in discerning what is pleasing to God. The values of human dignity and the common good must be considered. The Word of God, especially the life and message of Jesus, should be our guide. The collective wisdom of our Church and its moral tradition are available to assist us and should be carefully heard.

So we never need to stand alone in our decision making. We can face even thorny and complex situations with confidence. We are endowed with an intellectual capability of deciding, and we have at our disposal the resources to make our decision an informed one. Having done our best, we can be at peace knowing that we have done all that God requires.

We should do our best to inform our conscience and then to follow it.

For Reflection

- What sources have you drawn upon in the past when you were called upon to make a serious moral decision?
- How have these sources assisted you in making an informed decision of conscience?

The Ethics of Life and Death

by Marie Egan, I.H.M.

Marie Egan, IHM, a retired professor of religious studies, has taught at the college level for over twenty years. She holds a Doctorate in Sacred Theology from Catholic University of America in Washington, D.C. Marie is a member of the Immaculate Heart Community—a Christian lay ecumenical community. Among her other activities, Marie has been an active participant in interfaith dialogue and has been involved in health care delivery as a trustee of a Catholic hospital in southern California.

Birth and death, the edges of life, are moments charged with human feelings and emotion. They are moments that present some of the knottiest ethical problems and the most heart-wrenching moral decisions we face. There are other moments in between that also test our moral sensibilities.

Developments in modern medicine and technology have made these decisions increasingly difficult. A variety of techniques have been developed for ending life before birth and for extending life at its end. Science has made it possible to have sex without procreation and procreation without sex—to separate love making and baby making. Gene therapy may soon make it possible to shape the genetic blueprint of future generations, while human cloning threatens the very individuality that makes each of us unique before God.

It is because of such developments that people would do well to think through these issues before the urgent need for a decision presents itself. Today many are in search of ethical wisdom to guide them in decision making in our complex modern society. The Christian is no different, but the Christian is able to bring to these moral dilemmas a number of guiding convictions and time-honored principles.

The sanctity of human life. Christianity has always affirmed the basic value of life, recognizing each and every life as made in the image of a creative and loving God. Life is the primary gift of God to each individual. Pope Pius XII described it as the foundational good, the necessary condition for all other values, achievements, and relationships. Without physical life, no other human good is even possible. Thus, since physical life is so essential, health is a value and the promotion of preservation of health are worthy goals and moral responsibilities.

Human life is not an absolute good.

The Christian also recognizes that life is a relative, not an absolute, good, and the duty to preserve it is a limited one. Christianity does not demand the preservation of physical life at any cost. There are greater values worth the sacrificing of life. Jesus himself taught us this when he said, "No one has greater love than this, to lay down one's life for one's friends." (John 15:13) Jesuit moralist Richard McCormick asserts that life is of value precisely because of its potential for human relationships that make possible growth in love of God and neighbor. Life is good. Love is possible. Death is inevitable.

Death is part of the life cycle.

For the Christian, death is not the enemy; sin is. Accepting one's mortality is very much a part of Christian wisdom. As the Mass of Resurrection reminds us, in death life is changed, not taken away. Such a perspective sheds light on decisions about withholding or withdrawing treatment at the end of life when the treatment offers no hope for a return to meaningful existence. This decision is not one of abandonment. Rather, it manifests an acceptance of death as a natural part of the life cycle and the surrender of the dying into the hands of the loving God who first gave life.

Christianity does not demand the preservation of physical life at any cost.

Decisions surrounding momentous events in life—birth, death, reproduction, sickness, organ donation, human experimentation, care of defective newborns—are complex and taxing. The Christian can best prepare for these decisions by being as informed as possible about scientific and medical developments, by seeking guidance from the magisterium and the theological community, and by prayerfully reaffirming basic beliefs about the value of life, the inevitability of death, the assurance of resurrection, and the ongoing assistance of a loving God.

• • • For Reflection • • •

What principles described in this article will assist you when you are faced with bioethical dilemmas in your own life?

Social Sin and Grace

by Donna Toliver Grimes

Donna Toliver Grimes is an Education Specialist on the national staff of the Catholic Campaign for Human Development of the United States Conference of Catholic Bishops. She is a resource for diocesan staff who implement local CCHD transformative education efforts. Ms. Grimes develops resources and facilitates learning processes for adults and youth aimed at promoting Catholic social teaching and action, especially concerning poverty in the U.S. Formerly a parish director of religious education, she currently is a catechist and coordinator for the Confirmation program at her parish.

All sin has both personal and social implications. Sin is always the result of the actions and intentions of individuals. Such freely chosen attitudes and behaviors as dishonesty, malice, selfishness, and lust create negative consequences for others. They cause a breach in relationships, even when the source of harm is not revealed to all parties.

> The mystery of sin is composed of a twofold wound, which the sinner opens in his own side and in the relationship with his neighbor . . . At the bottom of every situation of sin there is always the individual who sins (CCC 117).

Sometimes, the damage that sin causes to our relationships extends beyond the individuals involved at the moment, beyond their spheres of concern and even beyond the span of their lifetimes. These sins create grave harm and have far-reaching consequences for the larger community and "can affect society and its institutions to create 'structures of sin' " (CCC, Glossary). This aspect of sin is known as social sin.

Most Catholics are familiar with original sin and with venial and mortal sins. Yet, the term *social sin* is relatively new in the Church's lexicon, coming into prominence in the 1980s, as bishops serving people in developing countries raised concerns about sinful structures in their societies. In 1983, Pope John Paul II convened a world synod of bishops at which several bishops from poorer countries spoke of the sinfulness of vast poverty, the oppression of certain groups of the population, civil strife, and many other areas of injustice.

Contemporary reflections notwithstanding, the concept of social sin actually has its origins in the Old Testament. We know that God entered into covenant relationships with individuals such as Abraham and Moses, as well as with the entire Israelite people. The Book of Deuteronomy, for example, speaks of generational sin by which the sins of the fathers (and mothers) pass down to their offspring for generations. (See Deuteronomy 5:9.) Likewise, there are numerous references in the

Old Testament to God's displeasure with the Israelites because of their disobedience, infidelity and mistreatment of the poor and vulnerable.

I have set before you life and death, the blessing and the curse. Choose life, then, that you and your descendants may live, by loving the LORD, your God, heeding his voice, and holding fast to him. (Deuteronomy 30:19–20)

Such sinful actions repeated over and over developed into sinful attitudes which spiritually poisoned the community. Over time, as these sinful attitudes grew they became entrenched and institutionalized. God then sent prophets to scold and redirect the people.

The history of God's people, both the Israelites and our own spiritual history, is the story of sin and redemption. Individually and collectively, we continue to sin against God and one another. We are often "a stiff-necked people . . . forever opposing the Holy Spirit" (Acts 7:51) who forget God's mercy and take for granted God's love. We regard entire classes of people as though they are outside the human family and beyond God's sphere of concern. Ultimately, social sin is the accumulation of personal sins which harm individuals and the community.

Social sin is every sin committed against the justice due in relations between individuals, between the individual and the community, and also between the community and the individual. (CCC 118)

Having identified some of the similarities between social and personal sin, note that social sin has its own distinguishing characteristics from personal sin. Two important distinctions between personal and social sin are that we *knowingly commit* personal sin, but can *unconsciously participate in* social sin. The tragedies of war, subjugation of peoples, excessive practice of materialism and consumerism, business methods that foster profit at any cost, the hoarding of the earth's resources that were created for all humankind—all of these are social sins. We participate in and in certain ways perpetuate sinful structures in the world, even without intending to do so.

A third significant distinction between personal and social sin concerns the path of reconciliation. When we personally sin against another person, the grace of the Sacrament of Reconciliation frees us from sin and repairs our relationship with God and hopefully with our offended brother or sister as well. In the case of personal sin we name the sin and promise to make amends for

> *We knowingly commit personal sin, but can unconsciously participate in social sin.*

it. We receive God's absolution along with the grace needed to maintain our resolve not to sin in this way again. What then is the method of reconciliation for social sin?

In the case of social sin our offenses tend to be less certain. For example, in many instances the actual harm is not fully disclosed or well understood. It may be difficult to pinpoint the source of sin or to determine the correction needed. Generally, we may not be able to identify the wrong until the ones who have been wronged inform us.

After identifying the sinful practices or structures, reconciliation for social sin takes the form of right or just actions that we take for the benefit of the larger community, for the common good, to help repair the breach in our relationships with others in society. Expressions of reconciliation for social sin include efforts to create just public policies, provide life-sustaining resources, heal past injustices, relieve the oppressed, advocate for the vulnerable, and help people to help themselves.

As Christians we understand that Christ lives within us and the Holy Spirit directs us. Furthermore, we are invited to participate in God's saving, sanctifying action. It is possible for us to receive the grace of reconciliation—a grace that is both personal and social, that reconciles us to God and to one another.

Our acceptance of this invitation brings us into a more fulfilling communion with God and the human family. We all benefit from greater justice and increased compassion, and, in the image of the Holy Trinity, loving, caring communities glorify God.

For Reflection

- Identify a modern day example of social sin. What attitudes and/or actions could cause us to unconsciously participate in this sin?
- Recall a time when you attempted to make amends for a social sin. What did you do and how did you experience social grace or reconciliation?

The Examination of Conscience

by Jo Rotunno

Every Catholic who has celebrated the Sacrament of Reconciliation has been introduced to the ancient practice of the examination of conscience—the review of our actions to determine their conformity to God's law. As far back as the New Testament, St. Paul reminded his Christian communities to consider their actions and ask God's forgiveness for their sins before participating in the Eucharist (See 1 Cor. 11:28–31). St. Anthony examined his conscience daily, and such daily scrutiny of one's actions was a part of the rule of the various monastic communities. St. Ignatius of Loyola called the daily examination of conscience the heart of his spiritual practice.

Today, fewer seem to use this ancient practice of the Church. Yet is an excellent way to examine the practice of our moral lives and to seek the guidance of the Holy Spirit as we try to do God's will. Here are some ideas for making the examination of conscience a part of your own spiritual practice.

1. **The Ten Commandments.** Use the Ten Commandments and the Precepts of the Church as the foundation for your examination of conscience, particularly before the celebration of the Sacrament of Reconciliation. However, try to take more than a minimalist approach. Move beyond the letter of the law.

2. **Sacred Scripture.** Follow the advice of the *Catechism of the Catholic Church* and use the word of God as a basis for scrutinizing your actions (CCC 1454). For example, imagine evaluating your own practice of forgiveness by reflecting on the story of the Forgiving Father (Luke 15:11–32).

3. **The Beatitudes.** An early Church document written by the Shepherd of Hermes in the second century A.D. recommended the Beatitudes as a standard for the moral life. The positive spirit of the Beatitudes and their roots in the values of Jesus make them an excellent norm for us today in the examination of conscience.

If the examination of conscience is already a part of your spiritual practice, consider one of the different approaches described here to help you examine your life with fresh eyes. If you have never formed this habit, now might a good time to begin.

Jo Rotunno serves as Director of Creative Development for RCL Benziger and is the project director for *Echoes of Faith Plus.* She has worked in Catholic schools, parish, and diocesan programs for more than thirty-five years. Her special interests are catechist and adult faith formation. Jo holds an MA in religious studies from Mount St. Mary's College in Los Angeles. She speaks on catechetical topics throughout the United States.

For Reflection

Which strategy for examining your conscience is most appealing to you? Why?

Resource Bibliography

Church Documents

Abbot, Walter M., SJ, gen. ed. *The Documents of Vatican II.* New York: Herder and Herder, 1966.

Benedict XVI. *Deus Caritas Est (God Is Love).* Vatican City: Libreria Editrice Vaticana, 2006.

———. *Spe Salvi (On Christian Hope.)* Vatican City: Libreria Editrice Vaticana. Washington, DC: USCCB, 2008.

Catechism of the Catholic Church, Second Edition. Libreria Editrice Vaticana. Washington, DC: United States Catholic Conference, 2000.

Compendium: Catechism of the Catholic Church. Washington, DC: United States Conference of Catholic Bishops, 2005.

Compendium of the Social Doctrine of the Church. Vatican City: Libreria Editrice Vaticana, 2004.

Congregation for the Clergy. *General Directory for Catechesis.* Vatican City: Libreria Editrice Vaticana, 1997.

Connell, Martin, ed. *The Catechetical Documents: A Parish Resource.* Chicago: Liturgy Training Publications, 1996.

International Commission on English in the Liturgy. *Book of Blessings: Study Edition.* Collegeville, MN: The Liturgical Press, 1989.

National Directory for Catechesis. Washington, DC: United States Conference of Catholic Bishops, 2005.

United States Catholic Catechism for Adults. Washington, DC: United States Conference of Catholic Bishops, 2006.

Theological Resources

Conners, Russell, Jr. and Patrick McCormick. *Choices, Character, and Community: The Three Faces of Christian Ethics.* Mahwah, N.J.: Paulist Press, 1998.

Cully, Iris V., and Kendig Brubaker Cully. *Harper's Encyclopedia of Religious Education.* San Francisco: Harper and Row, Publishers, 1990.

Gula, Richard, S.S. *The Call to Holiness: Embracing the Fully Christian Life.* Mahwah, NJ: Paulist Press, 2003.

———. *The Good Life: Where Morality and Spirituality Converge.* Mahwah, NJ: Paulist Press, 1999.

———. *Moral Discernment.* Mahwah, N.J.: Paulist Press, 1997.

———. *Reason Informed by Faith: Foundations of Catholic Morality.* Mahwah, NJ: Paulist Press, 1998.

Hardon, John A., S.J. *Modern Catholic Dictionary.* Garden City, Doubleday and Company, Inc., 1980.

Himes, Michael J. *Mystery of Faith: An Introduction to Catholicism.* Cincinnati, OH: St. Anthony Messenger Press, 2004.

Komonchak, Joseph A., Mary Collins, and Dermot A. Lane, ed. *The New Dictionary of Theology.* Collegeville: Michael Glazile, 1993.

Lucker, Raymond A., Patrick Brennan, and Michael Leach, eds. *The People's Catechism: Catholic Faith for Adults.* New York: Crossroad, 1995.

May, William E. *Introduction to Moral Theology,* Revised Edition. Huntington, IN: Our Sunday Visitor, 2003.

———. *Catholic Bioethics and the Gift of Human Life.* Huntington, IN: Our Sunday Visitor, 2000.

McBride, Alfred, O.P. *Essentials of the Faith: A Guide to the Catechism of the Catholic Church.* Huntington, Ind.: Our Sunday Visitor, Inc., 2002.

McCormick, Patrick. *A Banqueter's Guide to the All-Night Soup Kitchen of the Kingdom of God.* Collegeville, MN: Liturgical Press, 2004.

Shannon, Thomas, ed. *Bioethics. Revised.* Mahwah, N.J.: Paulist Press, 1993.

Sparks, Richard C., C.S.P. *Contemporary Christian Morality: Real Questions, Candid Responses.* New York: Crossroad, 1996.

Willems, Elizabeth. *Understanding Catholic Morality.* New York: Crossroad Herder, 1997.

Videos

The Mystery of Faith: An Introduction to Catholicism. A ten-part video series featuring Fr. Michael Himes. Fisher Productions, Box 727, Jefferson Valley, New York 10535.

Computer Resources

Catechism of the Catholic Church for Personal Computers. United States Catholic Conference, 1994. Available on disk and CD/ROM in English, Spanish, French.

Echoes of Faith ® *Plus*

Certificate of Completion

_____

Name

*has successfully completed the process
for the Catholic Morality module
in the Echoes of Faith Plus program.*

This certificate of completion is given at

_____

Parish

_____

Diocese

_____

Signature

_____

Date

Feedback Form

We hope that you have benefited from your use of this *Catholic Morality* module. Please take time to fill in your comments to the questions below. They will help the *Echoes of Faith Plus* team in planning additional resources to assist you in your ministry. If possible, discuss your responses with your program director before you mail it.

Thank you,
The *Echoes of Faith Plus* Team

1. What are the three most important insights or suggestions that you carry away with you as you complete this learning module *Catholic Morality?*

   _____

   _____

   _____

   _____

2. List up to five issues or questions that you would still like to discuss with your program director.

   _____

   _____

   _____

   _____

3. In a sentence or two describe how this learning module was helpful to you in your service as a catechist.

   _____

   _____

   _____

   _____

Tear out this sheet, fold and tape it closed, and return it to us. There is a business reply mechanism on the back of this page. Or you may fill out this survey online at www.EchoesofFaith.com. Thank you.

————————————————

————————————————

————————————————

BUSINESS REPLY MAIL

FIRST-CLASS MAIL   PERMIT NO 100   ALLEN TX

POSTAGE WILL BE PAID BY ADDRESSEE

ATTN PUBLISHER

ECHOES OF FAITH® PLUS PROJECT

RCL BENZIGER

PO BOX 7000

ALLEN TX 75013-9972

-- *Fold* --